THE CITY ON THE EDGE OF FOREVER

Hurled through the mysterious "Gateway of Forever", Dr. Leonard McCoy is sent back through time and space to the early 20th century where his actions will alter all future events and change all of Earth's history from that day forward.

Capt. Kirk and Mr. Spock have only one chance to put history back in its correct order. They too must enter the incredible Gateway and go back in time, and somehow find McCoy and STOP him, or else all life as they know it will cease to exist.

STAR TREK ™*

THE CITY ON THE EDGE OF FOREVER

written by **HARLAN ELLISON**

adapted from the television series
created by **GENE RODDENBERRY**

TM* DESIGNATES A TRADEMARK OF PARAMOUNT PICTURES CORPORATION

RLI: $\dfrac{\text{VLM 9 (VLR 5–9)}}{\text{IL 6+}}$

THE CITY ON THE EDGE OF FOREVER
A Bantam Book / November 1977

ISBN 0–553–11345–3

Published simultaneously in the United States and Canada

Bantam Books are published by Bantam Books, Inc. Its trademark, consisting of the words "Bantam Books" and the por-
trayal of a bantam, is registered in the United States Patent
Office and in other countries. Marca Registrada. Bantam
Books, Inc., 666 Fifth Avenue, New York, New York 10019.

PRINTED IN THE UNITED STATES OF AMERICA

0 9 8 7 6 5 4 3 2 1

DEAR READER,

After more than two years in preparation, Mandala Productions is both pleased and proud to present to you our first **Fotonovel** — a revolutionary approach to publishing in the United States. Our purpose from the beginning was to create a whole new concept — accurate and faithful recreations of your favorite television programs and movies.

But most innovative ideas are left as just that: *ideas.* And ours might have met the same fate had it not been for the support of the people from Paramount Pictures and Bantam Books. Their vast experience and belief in this new approach is in no small way responsible for our bringing to you this **Fotonovel,** our first of many.

We thank them most sincerely and invite you now to enter the world of Star Trek. Have a pleasant journey.

MANDALA PRODUCTIONS

ENCOUNTER WITH AN ELLISON

by Sandra Cawson

Harlan Ellison's home is a calculated fall down a rabbit hole. Every wall scintillates with original paintings by the Italian Campanile, the German Wünderlich, the Japanese Kanemitsu, Leo & Diane Dillon — who do the covers of his books. Every corner is jammed with sculpture and toys and books, my God! the books: 17,000 in a sprawling many-winged hillside retreat from which pour, every year, books, short stories, essays, reviews, motion picture scripts and, of course, award-winning teleplays.

Not the least of these high points of television drama is the *Star Trek* segment called "The City on the Edge of Forever." Winner of the Writers Guild of America award as the Most Outstanding Dramatic-Episodic Script for 1967-68, winner of the World Science Fiction Convention Achievement Award (the prestigious "Hugo", of which Ellison has won six, more than any other writer in the field) as the Best Dramatic Presentation of 1967, and winner of a George Méliès Fantasy Award at the International Film Festival in 1973, it is the single most popular show ever aired by *Star Trek.*

To my surprise and delight, I found Ellison to be outgoing, charming, hospitable and prepared to answer my most prying questions.

Sandra: Mr. Ellison—
Harlan: My name is Harlan. "Mr. Ellison" was my father. He died in 1949.
Sandra: Harlan. Why is "The City on the Edge of Forever" as well-loved as it seems to be by fans and critics alike?
Harlan: Because it's a story about people. The underlying philosophical theme carries the plot forward, but essentially it's a very simple love story. A story of choice. The kind of story that is identified traditionally as "tragedy" in the grand sense. I don't mean that to sound pompous or even to suggest that

it's literature — because after all, what we're talking about is still just a television segment — but it's the essence of human relationships that snares the viewer. It's what Faulkner intended when he spoke of the only thing really worth writing about being "the human heart in conflict with itself." I think those who like the show identify with that.

Sandra: I understand the version that won the Hugo was the aired version, and the one that took the Writers Guild award was your original version? Were they that different?

Harlan: In some very personal and, I still believe, more significant ways, yes. Very different.

Sandra: What ways?

Harlan: Well, you must understand that working in television can be a singularly crippling and brutalizing thing for the creative spirit, particularly if a writer perceives himself as something more than merely a hack or a creative typist who is helping to fill network airtime in order to sell new cars and deodorants. So a writer who cares about his work puts in small touches, special scenes, lines of enriching dialogue, that give him his reason for writing it. Almost all of those touches were excised in the name of straight action sequences. Their loss diminished the value of the script enormously. At least for me.

Sandra: But it's a *good* show, very beautiful.

Harlan: Only fifty per cent of what *could* have been filmed was presented; and if that fifty per cent knocks people out, imagine how they'd love the whole version.

And now, I hate to end this, but I'm writing the pilot for my own television series, and I'd like to get back to it.

Sandra: Thank you. It's been peculiar.

Harlan: And thank *you*. Yes, hasn't it?

Dan Tooker

CAST LIST

James T. Kirk, Captain
William Shatner

A man in his mid-30's, whose independent nature and compassionate heart make him a natural leader whose overriding concern is always the well-being of his ship and crew.

Spock, First Officer
Chief Science Officer
Leonard Nimoy

Of Vulcan and Terran heritage, which accounts for his analytical mind and extraordinary strength. His life is almost totally ruled by reason and logic.

Leonard McCoy, M.D., Lt. Commander
Senior Ship's Surgeon, Head of Life Sciences Dept.
DeForest Kelley

Though surrounded by the most advanced equipment the 25th century can offer, he still practices medicine more with his heart than his head.

Montgomery Scott, Lt. Commander
Chief Engineer
James Doohan

A middle-aged man of Scottish descent whose knowledge of the ship's engineering section is boundless.

Edith Keeler

Joan Collins

A very attractive
social worker

**Sulu,
Chief
Helmsman**

George Takei

living in the United
States in the
1930's, who runs
a mission and
devotes her
energies to those
less fortunate
than herself.

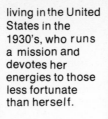

Navigator

Bill Blackburn

Policeman

Hal Boylor

**Uhura, Lt.
Communications
Officer**

Nichelle Nichols

Rodent

John Harmon

Guard

Michael Barrier

Lt. Galloway

David L. Ross

THE CITY ON THE EDGE OF FOREVER

SPACE: The Final Frontier

THESE ARE THE VOYAGES OF
THE STARSHIP ENTERPRISE.
ITS FIVE YEAR MISSION:
TO EXPLORE STRANGE NEW
WORLDS, TO SEEK OUT NEW
LIFE AND NEW CIVILIZA-
TIONS...TO BOLDLY GO
WHERE NO MAN HAS GONE
BEFORE.

Stardate: 3134.0

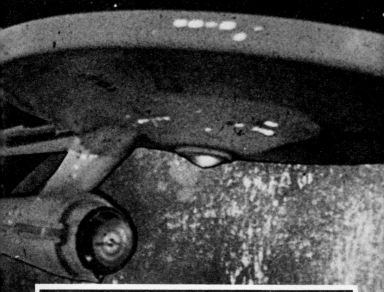

While on an investigative mission to an uncharted planet, the **Starship** **Enterprise** is suddenly jolted by an *unexpected force!*

Mr. Sulu . . .
What
was **that**?

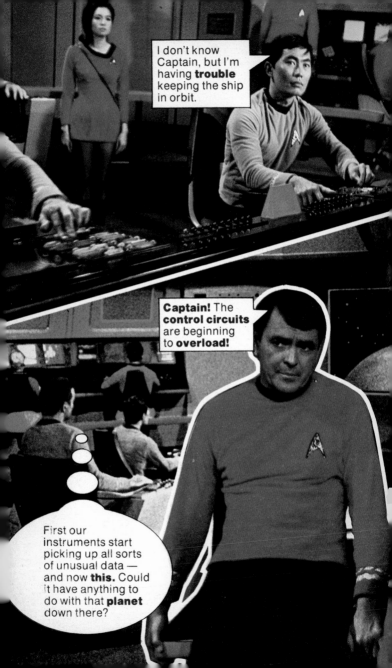

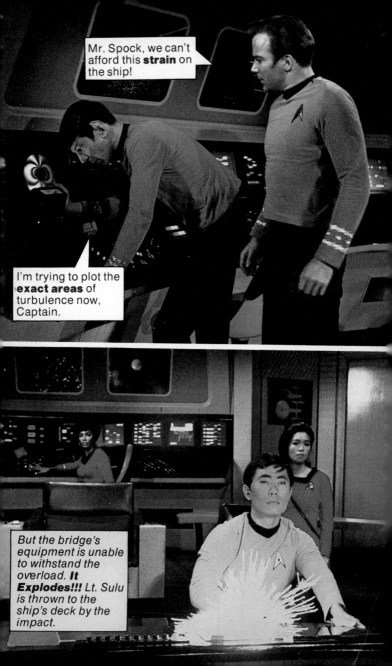

Kirk's reaction is **immediate!** Quickly he moves to his control panel and notifies the **Medical Department.**

Sickbay!
To the bridge!

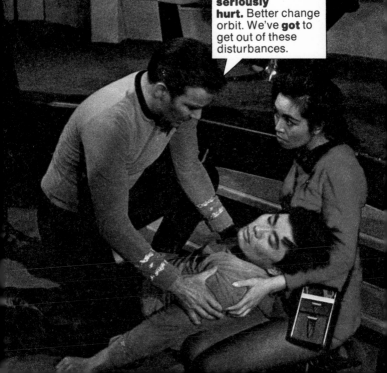

He rushes to Sulu.

I think he's **seriously hurt.** Better change orbit. We've **got** to get out of these disturbances.

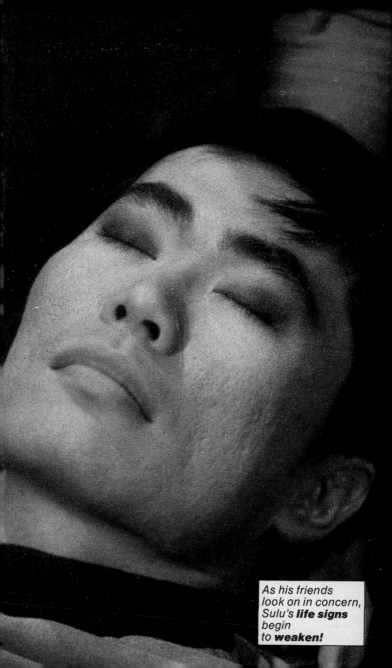

As his friends look on in concern, Sulu's **life signs** begin to **weaken!**

I'd better risk a few drops of **cordrazine.**

That's **tricky stuff!** Are you sure you want to risk . . .

*But the moment the hypo is injected, Sulu's eyes begin to open, and within **seconds** he regains consciousness and **completely recovers!** Everyone breathes a sigh of relief.*

You were about to make a **medical comment,** Jim?

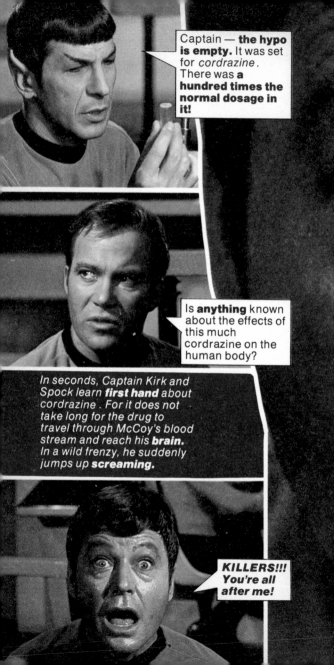

The crew members try to catch McCoy, but the cordrazine has given him **added strength.** Convinced that they are trying to kill him, he fights off their efforts and bolts for the door, escaping from the bridge.

Kirk, shocked by his friend's behavior, nevertheless remains in **complete charge.**

Alert Security. McCoy must be found before he hurts himself, or **anyone else.**

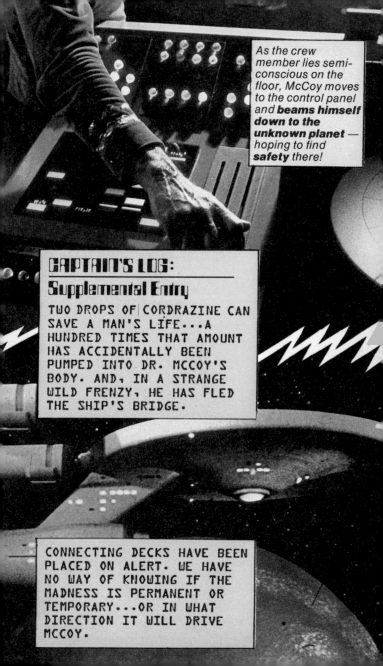

As the crew member lies semi-conscious on the floor, McCoy moves to the control panel and **beams himself down to the unknown planet** — hoping to find **safety** there!

CAPTAIN'S LOG:
Supplemental Entry

TWO DROPS OF CORDRAZINE CAN SAVE A MAN'S LIFE...A HUNDRED TIMES THAT AMOUNT HAS ACCIDENTALLY BEEN PUMPED INTO DR. MCCOY'S BODY. AND, IN A STRANGE WILD FRENZY, HE HAS FLED THE SHIP'S BRIDGE.

CONNECTING DECKS HAVE BEEN PLACED ON ALERT. WE HAVE NO WAY OF KNOWING IF THE MADNESS IS PERMANENT OR TEMPORARY...OR IN WHAT DIRECTION IT WILL DRIVE MCCOY.

A short time later Kirk returns to the bridge after having checked with the ship's Medical Department.

Continue Alert on decks 4 through 11. McCoy has **still** not been found!

The **Medical Department** knows as little as **we** do.

Library record tapes show that in dosages approaching this, there's some record of **wild paranoia.** Subjects become **hysterically convinced** that they are in **mortal danger.** They seek escape **at any cost** and are **extremely dangerous.**

Alert! Alert! This is Security!

The landing party is assembled and beamed down to the strange planet . . .

and into the **time displacement** which has caused so much trouble!

Spock — turn on the **Tricorder.**
On, Captain.
Detail — **fan out.** Begin looking for McCoy — no telling what his **state of mind** is.
As they move around the ruins, their eyes become riveted on an ***enormous structure*** *that* ***dominates*** *the landscape!*
What **is** that? It seems to be **pulsating** with some kind of **power.**

I see **no reason** for answers to be couched in **riddles.**

At an **incredible speed,** images are being flashed, tracing man's history from its **very beginning!**

*The **unlimited possibilities** offered by this Gateway to times past **fascinates** Kirk.*

Strangely compelling. . . To be able to step through that portal and **lose oneself in another world!**

Unnoticed by the others, McCoy regains consciousness. But with the cordrazine still in his system, he remains convinced that Kirk and the rest are trying to kill him. He studies the strange object that the others are watching.

A Doorway? My **only** chance. I **have** to try it!

Imagine . . . traveling back in time!

Fantastic!!

As the landing party stares in wonderment at the incredible images the Guardian is projecting, **McCoy makes a break for "freedom"** . . .

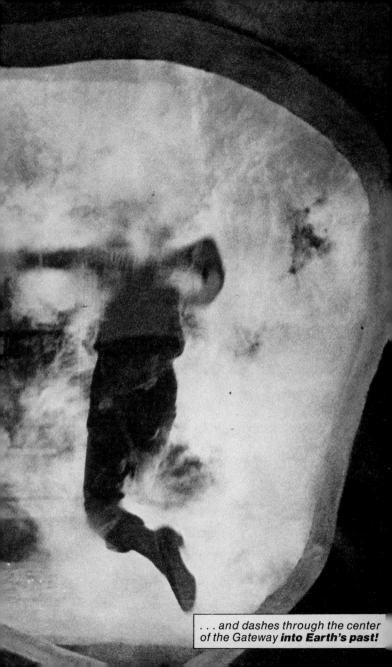

. . . and dashes through the center of the Gateway **into Earth's past!**

The instant McCoy's body passes through the Gateway, **he vanishes!** The crew is left staring in disbelief at an **empty space.** All smoke clears . . . and all images **disappear!**

He's **gone!**

Guardian — **where is Dr. McCoy?**

He has passed into **what was.**

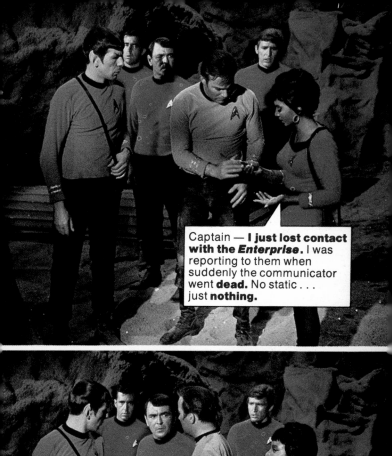

Captain — **I just lost contact with the *Enterprise*.** I was reporting to them when suddenly the communicator went **dead.** No static . . . just **nothing.**

Scotty, check this communicator.

There's **nothing wrong** with it, Sir.

CAPTAIN'S LOG:
No Stardate

FOR US, TIME DOES NOT EXIST.
MCCOY, BACK SOMEWHERE IN
THE PAST, HAS AFFECTED A
CHANGE IN THE COURSE OF TIME.
ALL EARTH'S HISTORY HAS
BEEN CHANGED. THERE IS NO
STARSHIP "ENTERPRISE." WE
HAVE ONLY ONE CHANCE – WE
HAVE ASKED THE GUARDIAN TO
SHOW US EARTH'S HISTORY
AGAIN. SPOCK AND I WILL GO
BACK INTO TIME OURSELVES
AND ATTEMPT TO SET RIGHT
WHATEVER IT WAS THAT MCCOY
CHANGED. SPOCK'S TRICORDER
WAS RECORDING THE GUARDIAN'S
IMAGES AT THE TIME MCCOY
ENTERED THE GATEWAY. IT WAS
A PERIOD OF AMERICAN HISTORY-
BACK IN THE 20TH CENTURY.

Guardian —
If we are successful . . .?
OLD ABE LINCOLN CAME OUT OF THE WILDERNESS
Then you will be returned. It will be as though none of you had gone. History will be restored.

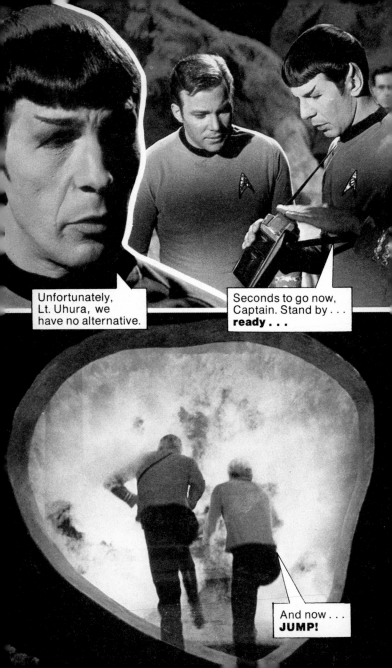

In a **fraction of a second** Kirk and Spock find themselves in **another era.**

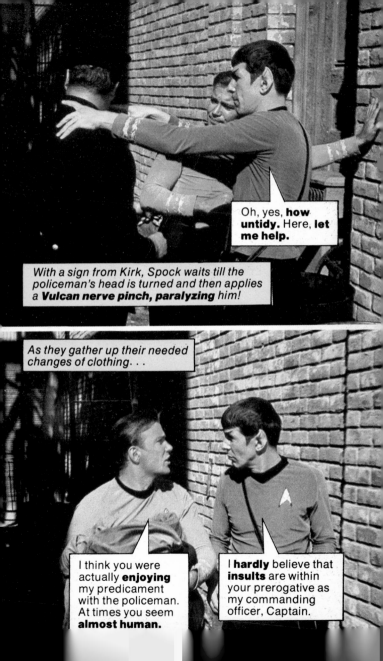

Spock and Kirk race up and down the unfamiliar streets, looking for some place to hide.

Realizing that their actions are attracting **considerable attention** they dash down a flight of stairs and through an **open door** into a basement.

Once inside, Kirk and Spock quickly change into the 1930's clothing.

Spock — have you made any **conclusions** yet?

We should have at least a **week** before McCoy arrives. But time is **too fluid** for me to be more precise.

Sorry . . . we were being **chased** by a policeman.
And **why** was that?
The more Kirk looks at her and hears her voice, the more he is taken with her.
She's **lovely.**
We **stole** these clothes. We didn't have any **money.**

Well, if its money you need, I **could** use some **help** around here — washing dishes, sweeping up, general cleaning . . . . I'll pay **15¢ an hour** for **10 hours** a day.

An **excellent** rate of payment . . . . But may I ask exactly where **are** we?

*After completing their chores, Spock and Kirk go upstairs to the mission's dining room where dinner is being served. Taking their bowls of hot soup and their slice of bread, they find two seats next to an extremely seedy looking man — **even by Depression standards!***

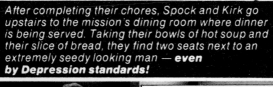

Not exactly a **sumptuous meal,** but at least it's **free.**

I wouldn't call it **free.** Pretty soon **Miss Goodie Twoshoes** will start her **preaching.**

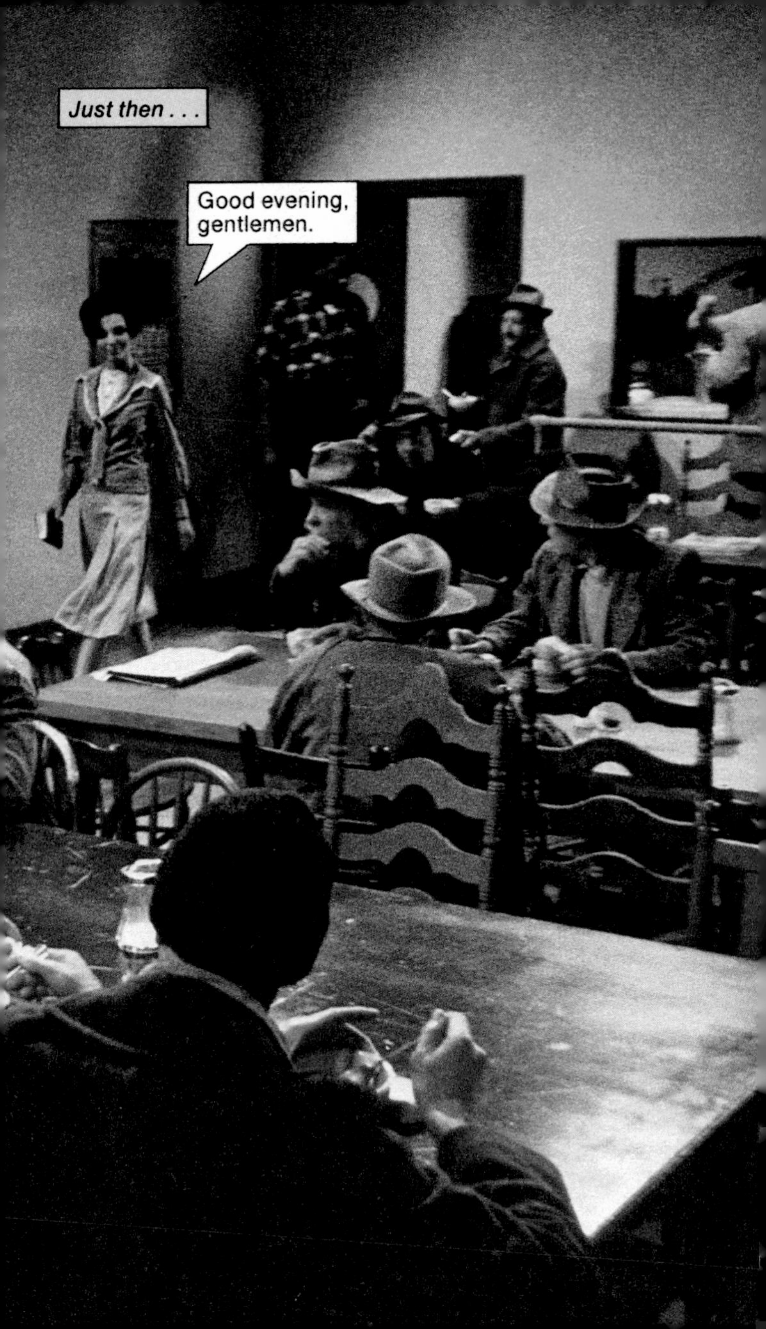
Just then . . .
Good evening, gentlemen.

And now, as I am sure someone has said, **"It's time to pay for the soup."** But let's get one thing **straight** first: **I'm no do-gooder.** If you're a **bum** — if you can't break off with the **booze** — then **get out.** As for the **rest** of you, I can't tell you how to find **happiness** when each day is a struggle just to **survive.** But the days **ahead** are worth waiting for. Things **are** going to get better.

In all my travels through the galaxy, I have **never met** such a woman.
I find her **most uncommon,** Mr. Spock.

Edith Keeler takes Kirk and Spock to a nearby rooming house where they rent their "flop" and settle in. But their problems are far from over. Their immediate and foremost concern is **MONEY.** Kirk must find some way to earn money — not only to pay for rent and food, but enough to buy the supplies Spock must have if he is to try to construct an **adapter** for the Tricorder. But these are **hard times.** Work — any kind of work — is **almost impossible** to come by. Men who once owned stores are reduced to selling their wares in makeshift shacks on the street. Men who once ran banks are now pulling pushcarts of vegetables. Fortunately, Kirk could not have found a better friend than Edith. Day after day, she **somehow** finds jobs for him and though they are not intellectually challenging, nevertheless they pay the bills. And while Kirk learns the correct way to **wash windows** and **shovel coal . . .**

. . . *Spock calls upon all of his **Vulcan powers** as he works **day and night** trying to construct the complex circuitry needed to change the Tricorder's data into actual pictures — the pictures that will pinpoint the **exact time and place** in which McCoy changed history. Then they'll at least have a chance of **stopping** him.*

*Early one afternoon Kirk returns to their room loaded down from a **shopping expedition** to the local market.*

I'm back, Spock. How's it going?

Spock — your cap! **Cover your ears.**

Jim, it's me — Edith.

Kirk opens the door slightly, trying to block Edith's view with his body.

Ah . . . Edith . . . good to **see** you.

If you can leave right away, I can get you five hours of work for 22¢ an hour . . . .

Even though Kirk's body obscures **most** of her vision, Edith is still able to catch sight of some of the **electrical equipment** in the room. Her eyes open wide. She has never seen such **strange and complicated** wiring and tubes and **can't imagine** what it is doing in their room.

What in the
is all that st
What are yo
up to?

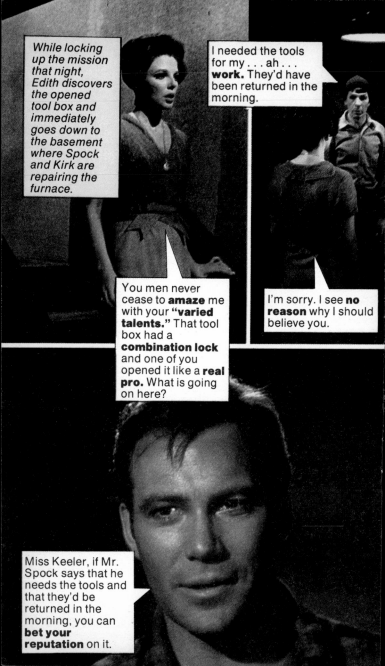

The following day, Spock **finally** manages to finish the complex equipment needed to turn the Tricorder's recordings into **actual pictures** . . .

And Edith Keeler appears on the screen in her **obituary.**

A few minutes later, Kirk returns from a job.

How are the **stone knives** and **bearskins?**

I think I have found our **focal point** in time. But I'm afraid I'm **overloading** the circuits. The picture keeps **fading away.**

It **does** smell like something's **burning.**

I'm getting a picture again. But I'm afraid you may find the news a bit **distressing.**

Let's see what you have.

But, as the static clears, a **different newspaper article** is seen on the screen.

EDITH KEELER

F. D. R. CONFERS WITH SLUM AREA "ANGEL"

Feb. 23, 1936—The President and Edith Keeler conferred for some time on her idea for a plan of action to the need

What's distressing about that? **It's fantastic! Franklin Delano Roosevelt** confers . . .

Just then the overloaded circuits *explode!*

Spock! The circuitry! It's burning up!

After the small fire is put out, Spock begins to try to repair the burnt-out equipment as Kirk mulls over what he has seen.

We actually **know** her **future.** Within six years she will become **so important** that even the **President** will seek her out.

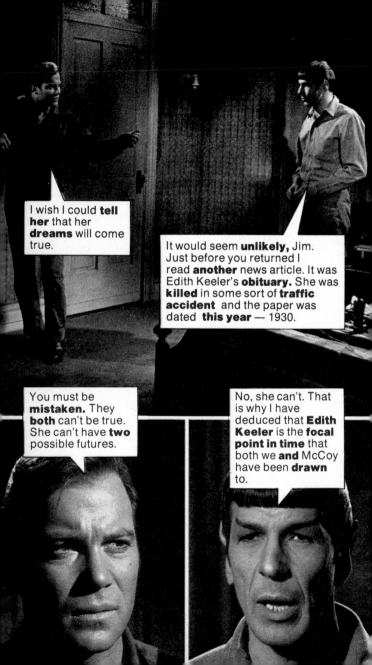

. . . And **all of history** will be changed depending on whether she **lives** or **dies?**

Yes! And McCoy is the **random element** that will affect **all history** — as **we** know it.

But in **his** condition, what does he do? . . . **kill her?**

Or does he **prevent** her from being killed?

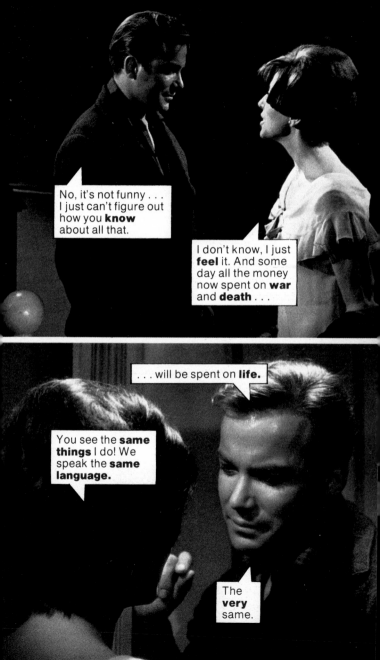

Nearby, the currents of time have finally swept Dr. McCoy to 1930. But where he is — or how he got there — McCoy has no idea.
The cordrazine still rules his mind. He remains convinced that his former friends are trying to kill him.
Assassins!!! You'll never get me!

*In his crazed state of mind, McCoy thinks that everything he sees is a **mental projection** set up to trick him. Running through the strange streets, he comes upon one of the bums from the mission.*

Have **you** escaped too? **Good** . . . we can **help** each other.

McCoy looks around the strange surroundings.

A perfect illusion! But where **are** we? A modern **museum? Explain** this trick.

*The bum is **too frightened** to speak.*

Finding McCoy's phaser, the bum begins to toy with the controls, unaware of its powers!

Accidentally, the bum sets the phaser on **"kill"** and in an instant he **vanishes forever** in a **blinding flash of light.**

Meanwhile, Kirk has returned to their room after his date with Edith.

Mr. Spock — how much longer before you'll have that working again?

I'll need at least two more days — with luck, one — before I **dare** make another attempt.

But Spock — for all we know, McCoy could have been here for a week **already.** Whatever he is going to do could happen tomorrow, or even **tonight.**

Captain, the last information we were able to get was achieved at the expense of over **30 hours of work** in burnt-out circuits.

But I **have to know** whether Edith **lives** or **dies.**

After coming to, McCoy has spent the night wandering the streets — constantly worried about his safety. Early the next morning, though, his fears begin to gently give way to exhaustion and hunger, when he sees the 21st Street Mission.

Edith, seeing the strange-looking man stumbling, goes to help . . .

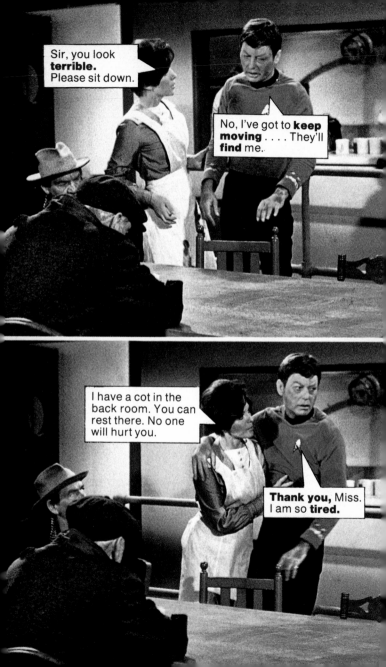

Germany? You mean Hitler won the Second World War?
Yes, because the peace movement delayed the U.S.'s entry.
SIEG HEIL! SIEG HEIL!

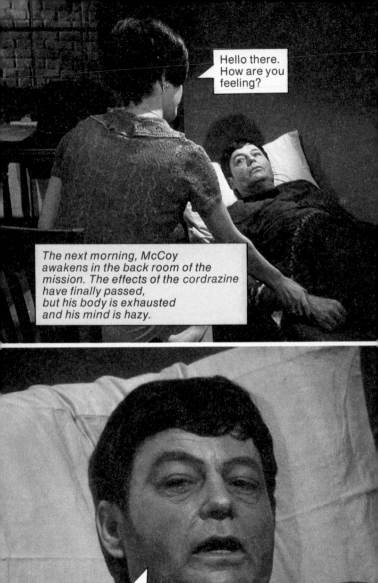

Hello there. How are you feeling?

The next morning, McCoy awakens in the back room of the mission. The effects of the cordrazine have finally passed, but his body is exhausted and his mind is hazy.

The most **common** question to ask would be **"Where am I?"** . . . . I don't think I'll ask it.

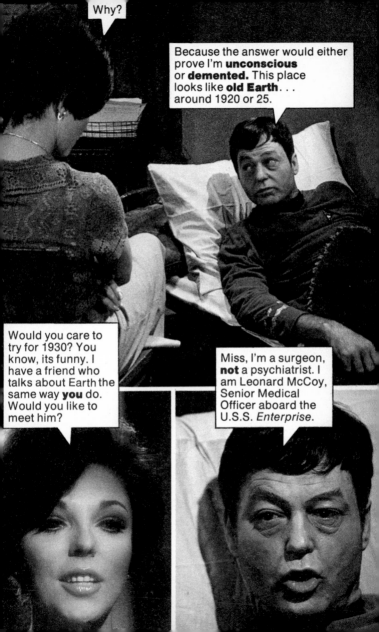

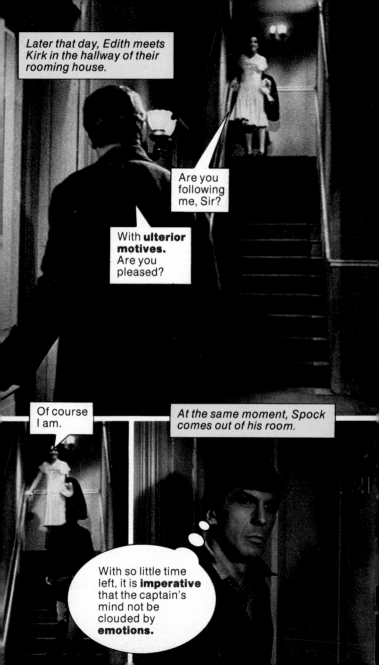

Suddenly Edith's foot slips! But before she falls down the stairs, Kirk **catches** her in his arms.
Oh . . .
Ah . . . .
Oh!

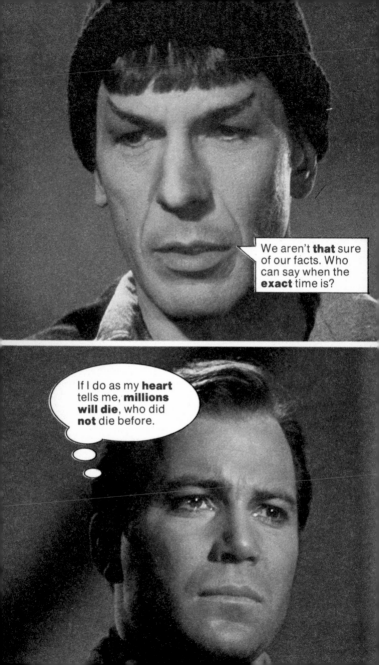

Spock dashes to meet Kirk.
What it is, Jim?
It's McCoy! He's **here** . . . **now!** In the . . .

At the same moment, having heard Kirk's voice, McCoy emerges.
Jim! Spock!
Bones! Are you all right?
Stay here? . . . **why?** I've **got** to find out what's going on over there.

Unaware of an approaching ***speeding truck,*** *Edith crosses the street.*

Kirk's *instant reflex* is to pull her to safety.

NO, JIM . . . DON'T!!!

Seeing McCoy also moving to help Edith, Kirk understands that this is the *exact moment* in which all history will be changed, and he realizes what he must do. Spinning around, he *desperately* grabs hold of McCoy!

Out of my way, Jim! LOOK OUT, EDITH! LOOK OUT!!!

*But history takes its toll. Edith is **brutally struck down** by the speeding truck!*

unbelievingly at Edith's twisted, broken body. But Kirk cannot **bear** to look.

You **deliberately** stopped me . . . **why???**

It's Edith Keeler.

Well, she's a **goner** . . . too bad.

Jeez . . . she was a **swell** dame.

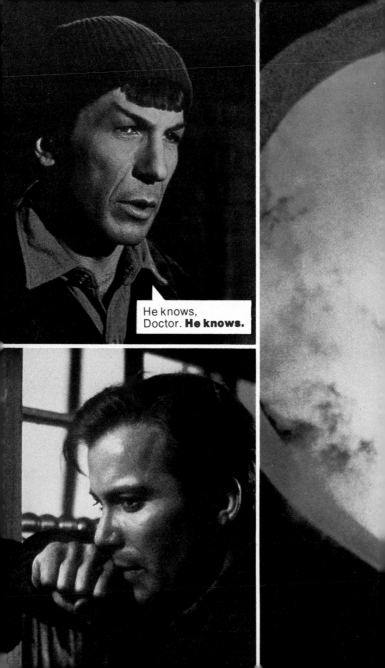

Having accomplished their mission, the landing party assembles and with Dr. McCoy...

...they are beamed back up to the Enterprise, *leaving behind the Gateway and the* **Guardian of Forever.**

Earth's history has been restored!

THE
END

GLOSSARY

Bridge — The top deck of the Starship from which the Captain, his chief officers and the navigator control the ship.

Communicator — Portable piece of equipment the size of a pack of cigarettes, used primarily for maintaining communication between landing parties on the surface of planets and the orbiting Starship.

Cordrazine — A drug used as a stimulant or energizer when administered in small doses, but capable of causing temporary behavior changes when administered in an overdose.

Gateway of Forever — Passageway through time and space with the ability to display images of history in chronological order. Anyone stepping through its vortex is instantaneously sent back to the exact period of time being shown, and their behavior in that time period affects the order of history.

Phasers — Personal weapons that have several adjustable settings ranging from "stun" to "kill" to "heat activator" to "dematerialize."

Ship's Log — Record keeping method of all activities aboard the Starship. Entries are made orally by the captain.

Sickbay — The area of the Starship where all major medical procedures are performed.

Stardate — Method of calculating time on board.

Star Fleet Command — Main headquarters for all space ship communications.

Transporter — Used for moving crew and/or cargo from the Starship to planets and back by changing the original molecular structure into energy which is beamed to a predetermined point, where the original molecular structure is reconstructed.

Tricorder — Portable, miniaturized computer capable of recording and analyzing all matter and storing such data, which can later be retrieved and displayed on the Starship's computer.

Turbolift — Elevator-type compartments connecting the 11 decks of the Starship, capable of moving horizontally and vertically and operated manually or by voice.

U.S.S. *Enterprise* — One of 13 starships with a crew of approximately 430. Its 11 decks contain a self-supporting mini-city.

Viewscreen — Electronic devices located throughout the ship that put crew members in visual contact with all other areas of the ship. The major viewscreen, located in the front of the bridge, is capable of displaying, at various magnifications, all matter in the ship's path.

Vulcan Nerve Pinch — A method of temporarily immobilizing humans, requiring knowledge of anatomy.

Vulcans — Race inhabiting the planet Vulcan, recognizable by their highly developed intelligence, pointed ears, upswept eyebrows and sallow complexion. Their lives are ruled by logic, not emotion.

Warp Drive — Method of propulsion exceeding the speed of light.

STAR TREK QUIZ

In each question below, circle the one answer that best completes the sentence.

1. **Gene Roddenberry may best be remembered for:**
   a. his starring role as Lt. Uhura
   b. creating Star Trek
   c. commandeering the USS *Enterprise*
   d. repairing the ship's energizers

2. **Edith Keeler's mission is located:**
   a. in Detroit
   b. on Skidrow
   c. on 21st Street
   d. in Watts

3. **A starship's primary means for defense are its:**
   a. transporters
   b. paragasts
   c. radiators
   d. deflectors

4. **In order to view the Tricorder's data, Spock needs:**
   a. batteries
   b. the Starship's computer
   c. integrating cables
   d. Scotty

5. **Cordrazine is a drug used primarily as:**
   a. a stimulant
   b. an antidote for radiation
   c. an aphrodisiac
   d. a tranquilizer

6. The Gateway of Forever:

   a. has complete control over its output
   b. was left behind by alien beings when their sun burned out
   c. can display images of the future
   d. is limited to presenting pictures in chronological order

7. A tribble is:

   a. a small furry creature
   b. a momentary loss in warp speed
   c. a 25th century slang term for liquor
   d. a communications computer

8. Scott's idea of a pleasant afternoon is:

   a. tinkering with some electronic gear
   b. playing three-dimensional dominoes
   c. reading up on Plato
   d. singing in the Starship's quartet

9. In time of emergency on board the Starship decisions are made by:

   a. the computer
   b. Capt. Kirk
   c. The United Federation of Planets regulatory ambassadors
   d. the Supreme Starship Commander

10. Edith Keeler must die or else:

   a. McCoy will never recover
   b. the United States will declare World War III
   c. the Tricorder will self-destruct
   d. Hitler will win World War II

Turn the page for the answers.

For centuries man has dreamt of the possibility of possessing **God-like qualities** — to be omniscient, all-powerful, all wise — to be able to control his environment and create new life.

But this dream has always remained locked in man's imagination — a fantasy — **unattainable.** Until suddenly it becomes a **reality.**

As the Starship *Enterprise* passes through a mysterious force-field, two crew members are strangely singled out and unexpectedly find themselves endowed with **supernatural powers** — powers that can control the destiny of all living beings . . . all objects . . . all matter. They are capable of doing anything they want — everything they want, and **no one, no thing can stop them.**

They have become **GODS.**

But will they use their "gift" to **benefit** mankind or **destroy** it?   What happens when humans tread **"Where No Man Has Gone Before"**?

Capt. Kirk and Mr. Spock and the entire crew of the U.S.S. *Enterprise* must face those questions, and the answers they find will affect **each one** of their destinies.

DON'T MISS:

"WHERE NO MAN HAS GONE BEFORE"

THE EXCITING REALM OF STAR TREK

☐ STAR TREK LIVES!
　　by Lichtenberg, Marshak & Winston　　2151　•　$1.95

☐ STAR TREK: THE NEW VOYAGES
　　by Culbreath & Marshak　　2719　•　$1.75

☐ SPOCK, MESSIAH! A Star Trek Novel
　　by Cogswell & Spano　　10159　•　$1.75

☐ THE PRICE OF THE PHOENIX
　　by Culbreath & Marshak　　10978　•　$1.75

THRILLING ADVENTURES IN INTERGALACTIC SPACE
BY JAMES BLISH

☐ SPOCK MUST DIE!　　10749　●　$1.50
☐ STAR TREK 1　　10835　●　$1.50
☐ STAR TREK 2　　10811　●　$1.50
☐ STAR TREK 3　　10818　●　$1.50
☐ STAR TREK 4　　10812　●　$1.50
☐ STAR TREK 5　　10840　●　$1.50
☐ STAR TREK 6　　8154　●　$1.25
☐ STAR TREK 7　　10815　●　$1.50
☐ STAR TREK 8　　10816　●　$1.50
☐ STAR TREK 9　　11285　●　$1.50
☐ STAR TREK 10　　10796　●　$1.50
☐ STAR TREK 11　　8717　●　$1.25

Buy them at your local bookstore or use this handy coupon for ordering:

Bantam Books, Inc., Dept. ST, 414 East Golf Road, Des Plaines, Ill. 60016

Please send me the books I have checked above. I am enclosing $_____
(please add 50¢ to cover postage and handling). Send check or money order
—no cash or C.O.D.'s please.

Mr/Mrs/Miss _____

Address _____

City_____State/Zip_____
　　　　　　　　　　　　　　　　　　　　　　　　ST—10/77
Please allow four weeks for delivery. This offer expires 10/78.